Editorial method

Small inconsistencies and errors in both text and music have been corrected without comment. Editorial hairpins are crossed thus: ⇥. Other editorial additions, including cautionary accidentals, suggestions of tempo, expression marks and dynamics are

placed within s‹
tings of *Ave veru*
expression are e

[1] J-M Nectoux, *Gabriel Fauré: a musical life*, transl. Nichols (Cambridge 1991).

EINLEITUNG

Während der zweiten Hälfte des 19. Jahrhunderts war die Kirchenmusik in den beliebten Kirchen von Paris durch die Vorherrschaft sentimentaler Melodik und Harmonik charakterisiert, die ihre Herkunft aus Salonmusik und Oper nicht verbarg, während die Tradition des Gregorianischen Chorals und der Mehrstimmigkeit der Renaissance vernachlässigt wurde. Sowohl Saint-Saëns (1835-1921) als auch Fauré (1845-1924) waren in der bekanntesten Kirche tätig, der Madeleine, Gemeinde-Kirche des Elysée. Die beiden Komponisten dienten der Kirche über einen Zeitraum von fast 50 Jahren, Saint-Saëns von 1857 bis 1877 als Organist, Fauré – er war einstmals Klavierschüler von Saint-Saëns – von 1877 bis 1905, zunächst als Kapellmeister (*maître de chapelle*), von 1896 an als Organist. Beide Musiker, die bis ans Ende ihres Leben enge Freunde waren, waren hervorragende Organisten. Während Fauré allerdings wenig Freude am Spiel hatte, genoß Saint-Saëns internationalen Ruf als virtuoser Interpret. Beide sahen in ihrer Tätigkeit bei der Madeleine wenig mehr als eine finanzielle Sicherung ihres Lebensunterhaltes, um ihren kompositorischen Arbeiten nachgehen zu können, und beide hatten wenig Sinn für religiöse Fragen. In seinem Buch *Problèmes et Mystères* gibt Fauré ein deutliches Bild seiner atheistischen Einstellung, und auch Fauré war wohl kaum gläubiger. Mit großer Erleichterung gaben beide Komponisten schließlich ihre kirchlichen Ämter auf, Saint-Saëns, nachdem er sich durch seine Konzerttätigkeit und seine Kompositionen finanzielle Unabhängigkeit geschaffen hatte, Fauré nach seiner Ernennung zum Direktor des Pariser Conservatoire.

Vor diesem Hintergrund entstanden die in der vorliegenden Ausgabe versammelten sechs Motetten. Es sind alles Gelegenheitswerke, die den in der damaligen Pariser Kirchenmusik vorherrschenden Stil widerspiegeln. Mit Ausnahme von Faurés *Ave Maria* wurden die Werke wohl mit Sicherheit zur Aufführung in der Madeleine geschrieben. *Ave Maria* und *Tantum ergo* von Saint-Saëns wurden etwa 1860 geschrieben, das *Ave verum* um 1863. Fauré komponierte sein *Tantum ergo* und das *Ave verum* im Jahr 1894, das auf einer früheren Fassung von 1877 beruhende *Ave Maria* wurde 1906 abgeschlossen. In einem Brief an seinen Verleger schreibt Fauré über dieses Werk: "Die Motette ist eher für eine kleine Kapelle oder für einen Salon gedacht als für eine große Kirche. Ich kann mir die Motette besonders gut im chorischen Unterricht für junge Damen vorstellen und ich rechne darauf, daß Madame Trélats Schülerinnen das Werk verbreiten werden."[1]

Zur Aufführung

Die Motetten zeichnen sich durch eine Grazie und einen Charme aus, die von Ausführenden und Publikum gleichermaßen begrüßt werden dürften. Sie sind hier zusammengefaßt, um eine Reihe alternativer Programmzusammenstellungen zu ermöglichen. Obwohl in beiden Fassungen des *Tantum ergo* solistische Stimmen ausgewiesen sind, können die Werke auch durchgehend mit vollem Chor besetzt werden (s. die Fußnoten bei jeder Motette). Klavierbegleitung ist als Alternative zur originalen Besetzung mit Orgel durchaus denkbar; für diesen Fall wurden herausgeberische Vorschläge hinsichtlich des Pedalgebrauchs und Oktavierungen in der linken Hand gemacht. Obwohl die Stücke nicht besonders schwierig sind, benötigen sie doch einige Sorgfalt bei der Aufführung. Die Vortragsanweisungen hinsichtlich Tempo und Ausdruck sollten sorgsam geprüft werden, um Sentimentalität oder Rührseligkeit zu vermeiden und um eine gute Balance zwischen einem einerseits zu kräftigen, opernhaften Tonfall und einem zu nüchternen Klang auf der anderen Seite zu erzielen. Phrasierungszeichen in den Vokalstimmen sollten lediglich als Hinweise zur Artikulation behandelt werden; nur in manchen Fällen sind sie Atemzeichen und sollten keinesfalls den musikalischen Fluß unterbrechen. Die Wortakzente im lateinischen Text sollten sorgfältig befolgt werden, um das *Sostenuto* zu erreichen, das so sehr ein Stilelement dieser Musik ist. Für solche Musiker, die sich bei der Aussprache des Lateinischen nicht ganz sicher sind, wurden im unten abgedruckten Text einige Betonungsakzente ergänzt. Die Motetten verlangen die gleiche klangliche Modulationsfähigkeit, wie man sie bei der Interpretation von Liedern der beiden Komponisten anstreben würde.

Quellen

Die Ausgabe basiert auf Drucken und Autographen der Bibliothèque Nationale, und zwar für Saint-Saëns (alle drei Werke), Durand et Fils (1885). Fauré: *Ave Maria*, Heugel & Cie (1910), arr. Henri Busser und BN MS17737; *Tantum ergo*, J Hamelle (1894); *Ave verum*, J Hamelle (1894) und BN MS17739.

Zur Editionstechnik

Kleinere Unstimmigkeiten und Fehler sowohl im Text wie in der Musik wurden kommentarlos verbessert. Vom Herausgeber ergänzte Decrescendo-Zeichen werden wie folgt gekennzeichnet: ⊐═══ . Alle anderen editorischen Zusätze (Warnungs-Akzidentien, Vorschläge zum Tempo, Vortragsanweisungen und dynamische Hinweise) sind mit Ausnahme der beiden *Ave verum* -Kompositionen, in denen alle dynamische Hinweise und Vortragsbezeichnungen herausgeberische Ergänzung sind, in eckige Klammern gesetzt.

Timothy Brown
Juni 1994

[1] J.-M.Nectoux, *Gabriel Fauré: les voix du claire-obscur* (1990) (übersetzt nach der englischen Ausgabe des Werkes, Cambridge 1991).

Latin texts

(unless otherwise indicated, the stress always falls on the first syllable of two-syllable words)
(falls nicht anders angegeben, wird jeweils die erste Silbe zweisilbiger Worte betont)

Ave María, grátia plena, Dóminus tecum: benedícta tu in muliéribus, et benedícta fructus ventris tui, Jesu(s). Sancta María, mater Dei, ora pro nobis peccatóribus, nunc et in hora mortis nostræ. Ámen.

Tantum ergo Sacraméntum
Venerémur cérnui,
Et antíquum documéntum
Novo cedat rítui,
Præstet fides suppleméntum
Sénsuum deféctui.

Genitóri, genitóque
Laus et jubilátio,
Salus, honor, virtus quoque
Sit et benedíctio,
Procedénti ab utróque
Compar sit laudátio. Ámen.

Ave, verum corpus natum de María Vírgine:
Vere passum, immolátum in cruce pro hómine:
Cujus latus perforátum fluxit aqua et sánguine (*or* unda fluxit cum sánguine):
Esto nobis prægustátum mortis in exámine.
O Jesu dulcis, O Jesu pie, (O Jesu fili Maríæ,) tu nobis miserére. (Ámen.)

English translations

Ave Maria
Hail Mary, full of grace, the Lord is with thee. Blessed art thou amongst women, and blessed is the fruit of thy womb, Jesus. Holy Mary, mother of God, pray for us sinners now, and in the hour of our death. Amen.

Tantum ergo
Therefore we, before him bending
This great sacrament revere:
Types and shadows have their ending,
For the newer rite is here;
Faith, our outward sense befriending,
Makes the inward vision clear.

Glory let us give and blessing
To the Father and the Son,
Honour, might and praise addressing,
While unending ages run;
Ever too his love confessing,
Who, from both, with both is one. Amen.

Ave verum Hail, true body, of the Virgin Mary born, which in anguish to redeem us disd't suffer upon the cross; from whose side, when pierced by the spear, there came forth both water and blood: be to us at our last hour the source of consolation. O loving Jesu, O holy Jesu, O Jesu thou Son of Mary, have mercy on me. Amen.

Übersetzungen

Ave Maria Gegrüßet seist Du, Maria, voll der Gnade, der Herr ist mit Dir, Du bist gebenedeit unter den Frauen und gebenedeit ist die Frucht Deines Leibes, Jesus. Heilige Maria, Mutter Gottes, bitte für uns Sünder, jetzt und in der Stunde unseres Todes. Amen.

Tantum ergo Laßt uns solch großes Sakrament tiefgebeugt verehren! Dieser Bund wird ewig währen und der alte hat ein End. Unser Glaube soll uns lehren, was die Sinne nicht erkennen. Gott dem Vater und dem Sohne sei Lob und Preis, Heil, Kraft und Ehre dargeboten, wie auch dem von diesen beiden ausgehenden Heiligen Geist. Amen.

Ave verum Gegrüßet seist du, wahrer Leib, geboren von Maria der Jungfrau, der wahrhaftig gelitten hat, am Kreuz geopfert wurde für die Menschen, aus dessen durchbohrter Seite Blut und Wasser geflossen ist: Sei uns Stärkung in der eigenen Todesstunde. O süßer Jesus, o heiliger Jesus, O Jesus, Sohn Mariens, erbarme Dich unser. Amen.

This edition © 1994 by Faber Music Ltd
First published in 1994 by Faber Music Ltd
3 Queen Square London WC1N 3AU
Cover design by S & M Tucker
Music processed by Chris & Gail Hinkins
German translations by Dorothee Göbel
Printed in England by Halstan and Co Ltd
All rights reserved

ISBN 0 571 51483 9

Choral Programme Series

Consultant Editor: Simon Halsey

Fauré & Saint-Saëns

SIX MOTETS
FOR UPPER VOICES

AVE MARIA · TANTUM ERGO · AVE VERUM

(SA/Organ or Piano)

EDITED BY TIMOTHY BROWN

FABER $f\!f$ MUSIC

CONTENTS

INTRODUCTION

During the latter half of the nineteenth century, religious music in the fashionable churches of Paris was characterized by a prevalence of sentimental melody and harmony which owed more to the music of the salon or the opera-house than it did to the neglected heritage of Gregorian chant and renaissance polyphony. Both Saint-Saëns (1835-1921) and Fauré (1845-1924) worked in the most fashionable church of them all, the Madeleine, parish church of the Elysée. Between them they served the church for almost fifty years, Saint-Saëns from 1857 to 1877 as organist, and Fauré (who was once his piano pupil) from 1877 to 1905, first as choirmaster (*maître de chapelle*) then, from 1896, as organist. The two musicians, who were close and life-long friends, were fine organists; whilst Fauré found little joy in the instrument, Saint-Saëns enjoyed an international reputation as a virtuoso player. Both, however, regarded their employment at the Madeleine as little more than a way of earning a living in order to support their activities as composers. Neither had much time for religion. In his book *Problèmes et Mystères*, Saint-Saëns powerfully demonstrated his atheism; Fauré was scarcely more devout. It was with immense relief that the two composers eventually resigned from their church positions, Saint-Saëns on achieving financial independence through his recital work and composition, and Fauré on his appointment as Director of the Paris Conservatoire.

This then was the background to the composition of the six motets included in this volume. All are 'occasional' works, reflecting the prevailing style of Parisian church music. With the exception of Fauré's *Ave Maria*, they were almost certainly composed with performance at the Madeleine in mind. *Ave Maria* and *Tantum ergo* by Saint-Saëns were composed c.1860, and *Ave verum* c.1863. Fauré's *Tantum ergo* and *Ave verum* were composed in 1894; *Ave Maria*, based on an earlier version of 1877, was completed in 1906. In a letter to his publisher, Fauré wrote of this motet: '[it] is by its nature destined more for the chapel or salon than for a large church. I see its future lying especially in the choral classes for young ladies and I'm counting on Mme Trélat's fair pupils to launch it.'[1]

Performance

All the motets possess a grace and charm which will be enjoyed by singers and audiences alike, and in this collection they are presented so as to offer a number of alternative programming options. Although solo voices are specified in both settings of *Tantum ergo*, the music is equally successful if performed *full* throughout (see footnote for each motet). Piano accompaniment is a perfectly acceptable alternative to the originally-specified organ, and a few editorial suggestions concerning the use of sustaining pedal and left hand are included. Though not especially complicated, the pieces require some care in performance. To prevent sentimentality or mawkishness, tempi and expression marks need to be handled judiciously, and a balance struck between a tone that is neither too full-blooded and operatic on the one hand nor too 'antiseptic' and bland on the other. Apostrophes in the vocal parts should be interpreted as nothing more than articulation markings; only occasionally intended to indicate breaths, they should never be allowed to break the musical flow. Sensitivity to the word stress of the Latin texts will help to give shape to the *sostenuto* phrasing which is so much a feature of the style of this music. To assist those unfamiliar with the pronunciation of Latin, some stress accents have been added to the text, printed in full below. In general, the motets will benefit from being sung with the flexibility one would bring to a performance of songs by the same composers.

Sources

These editions are based on printed sources and autograph copies in the Bibliothèque Nationale, Paris, as follows: Saint-Saëns (all three works), Durand et Fils (1885); Fauré *Ave Maria*, Heugel & Cie (1910), arr. Henri Busser, and BN MS17737; *Tantum ergo*, J Hamelle (1894); *Ave verum*, J Hamelle (1894), and BN MS17739.

Ave Maria

Text: Medieval Marian antiphon, based on Luke I:42

CAMILLE SAINT-SAËNS

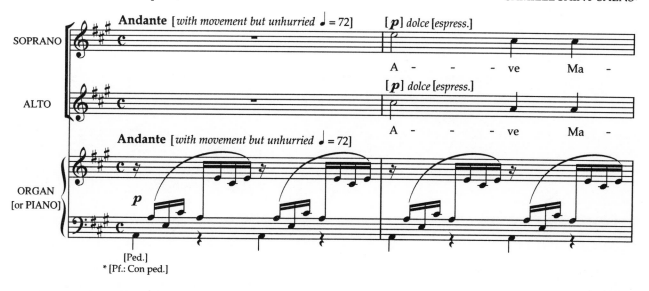

* If played on the piano, the left hand bass notes may be reinforced with the lower octave *ad lib.*
  Bei der Aufführung mit Klavier können die Noten der linken Hand (nur die tiefen Töne), nach unten oktaviert werden.

4

* Composer's articulation markings: see Introduction.
  Zu den Artikulationsbezeichnungen des Komponisten: siehe Einleitung.

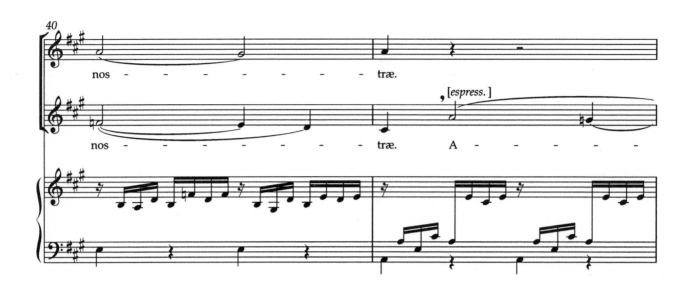

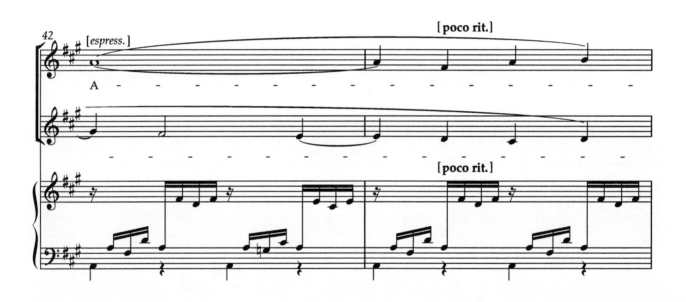

to Monsieur J. Lecocq

Tantum ergo

Text: Hymn by St. Thomas Aquinas

CAMILLE SAINT-SAËNS

* May be performed full throughout.
Kann durchgehend chorisch ausgeführt werden.

11

* If sung full throughout, this part may be omitted.
  Wenn das Stück durchgehend chorisch ausgeführt wird, kann diese Melodielinie weggelassen werden.

Ave verum

Text: Medieval sequence for Corpus Christi

CAMILLE SAINT-SAËNS

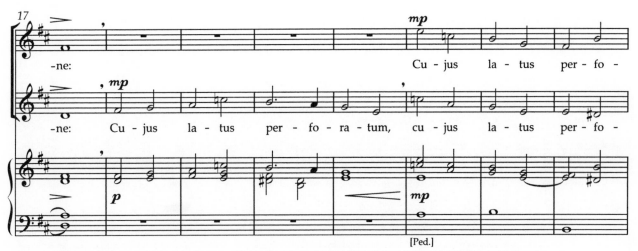

* All dynamics and marks of expression are editorial. *Alle dynamischen Angaben und Vortragsanweisungen sind Zusätze des Herausgebers.*
† Composer's articulation markings: see Introduction. *Zu den Artikulationsbezeichnungen des Komponisten: siehe Einleitung.*

14

to Madame Georges Kinen

Ave Maria

Text: Medieval Marian antiphon, based on Luke I:42

GABRIEL FAURÉ Op. 93

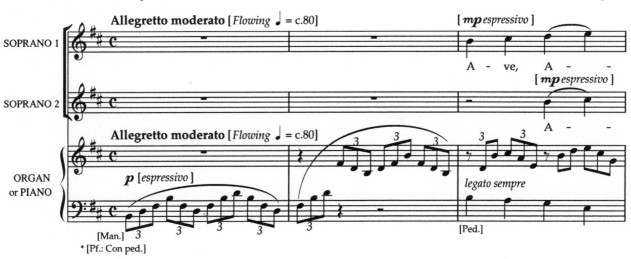

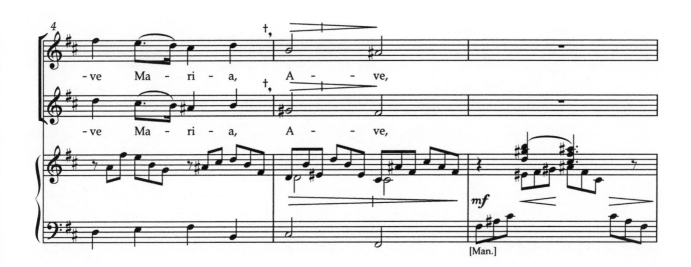

* If played on the piano, left hand passages marked 'ped.' may be reinforced with the lower octave *ad lib.*
Bei der Aufführung mit Klavier können die Passagen der linken Hand, die mit 'ped.' gekennzeichnet sind, nach unten oktaviert werden.
† Composer's articulation markings: see Introduction.
Zu den Artikulationszeichnungen des Komponisten: siehe Einleitung.

* F♯ in source. *Fis in der Quelle.*
† *Ossia* notes are Fauré's. *Die Ossia–Fassung stammt von Fauré.*

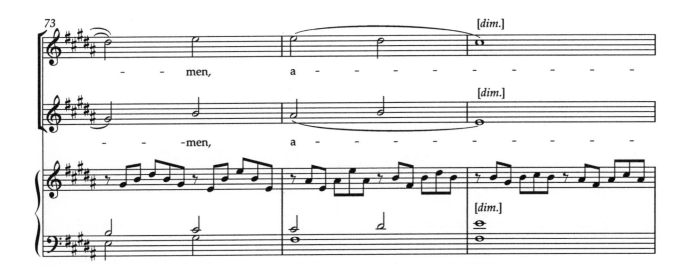

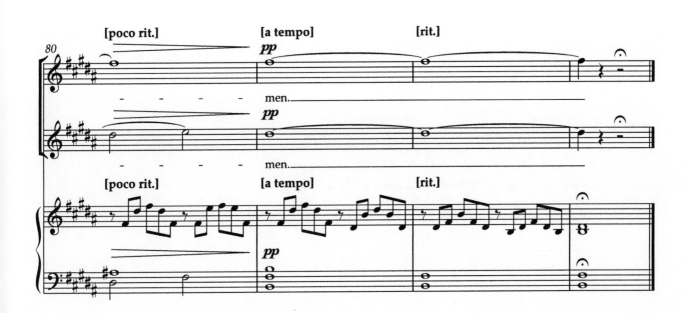

Tantum ergo

Text: Hymn by St Thomas Aquinas

GABRIEL FAURÉ Op.65 No.2

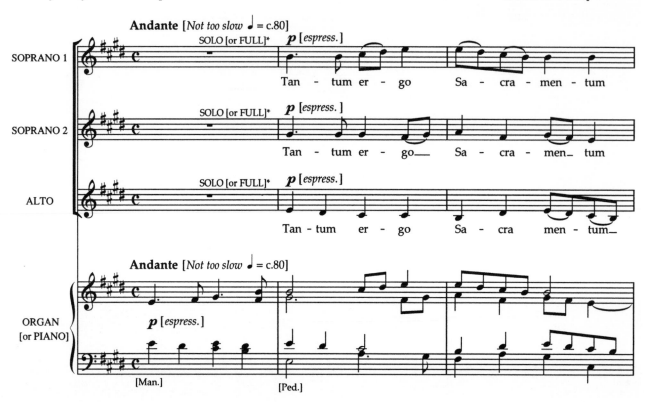

* May be performed full throughout.
Kann durchgehend chorisch ausgeführt werden.

* Words from bar 12 to bar 15 are editorial, completing the hymn text. Source repeats words of bars 8–11.
  *Der vom Herausgeber ergänzte Text von T.12 bis T.15 vervollständigt den Choraltext.
  In der Quelle werden hier die Worte aus den Takten 8–11 wieder holt.*

† ♮ in original / *im Original.*
‡ ♭ in original / *im Original.*

24

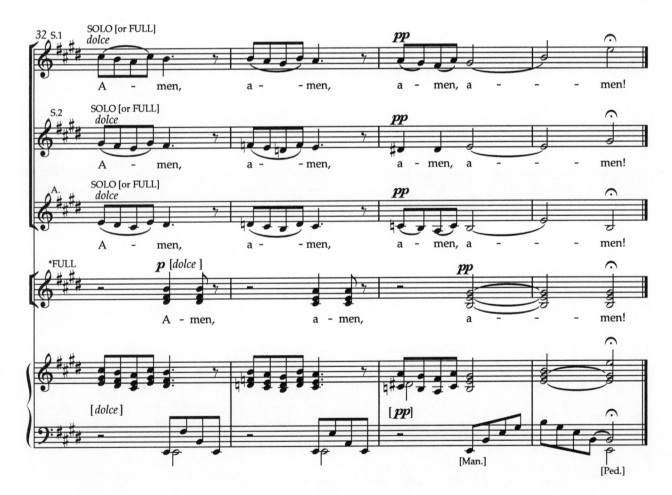

Ave verum

Text: Medieval sequence for Corpus Christi

GABRIEL FAURÉ Op.65 No.1

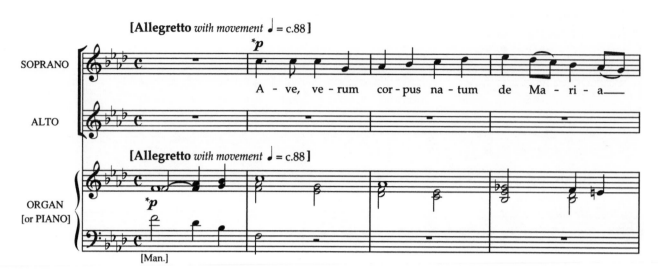

* All dynamics and marks of expression are editorial.

Alle dynamische Angaben und Vortragsanweisungen sind Zusätze des Herausgebers.

† Original underlay:

Die Textunterlegung des Original ist wie folgt:

in— cru- ce pro ho-mi-ne,

* ♪ in source. ♪ im Original.

* ♪ in source. ♪ im Original.

Reproduced and printed by
Halstan & Co. Ltd., Amersham, Bucks., England

Choral Programme Series

For upper voices:

Fauré & Saint-Saëns – Six Motets SA/organ or piano

Franz Schubert – Three Partsongs SSAA/piano

Robert Schumann – Eight Partsongs SA/piano & SSA/piano

English Edwardian Partsongs SSA/piano

Schwartz – Choruses from 'Godspell' and 'Children of Eden' SSA/piano

Lloyd Webber – Memory and other choruses from 'Cats' SSA/piano

Lloyd Webber – Mr Mistoffelees and other choruses from 'Cats' SSA/piano

For mixed voices:

Benjamin Britten – Christ's Nativity SATB (div)

French Chansons – Saint-Saëns/Fauré/Debussy SATB & SATB/piano

Antonín Dvořák – Four choruses for mixed voices Op 29 SATB

Gustav Holst – Five Partsongs Op 12 SATB

Felix Mendelssohn – Four Sacred Partsongs SATB (div)

C.H.H. Parry – Seven Partsongs SATB

Franz Schubert – Four Partsongs SATB/keyboard

C.V. Stanford – Seven Partsongs SATB

Ralph Vaughan Williams – Three Choral Hymns SATB/organ or piano

Gilbert & Sullivan – Opera Choruses 1 SATB/keyboard

Gilbert & Sullivan – Opera Choruses 2 SATB/keyboard

Five English Folksongs SATB

Five American Folksongs SATB

A Gospel Christmas – Spirituals for the festive season SATB/piano

Schwartz – Gospel choruses from 'Godspell' and 'Children of Eden' SATB/piano

Lloyd Webber – Memory and other choruses from 'Cats' SATB/piano

Lloyd Webber – Mr Mistoffelees and other choruses from 'Cats' SATB/piano

ISBN 0-571-51483-9

Faber Music 3 Queen Square London WC1N 3AU